Contents

Three short plays for three parts – each with the same start, but with very different endings.

Fishy Starter

Scene: Rod and Pippa enter a gloomy pub.

Rod   This pub will do.

Pippa   It doesn't look very nice.

Rod   It doesn't matter. It's out of the rain.

Pippa   I don't think it's open.

Rod   It's somewhere to sit. I need to talk to you.

Pippa   I don't like the smell.

Rod   It's fine. I just need to talk.

Pippa   There's a better pub over the road.

Rod   I need to tell you something.

[*A waiter appears as if from nowhere. Pippa jumps*]

Waiter   Can I help you?

Pippa   Aah! You scared me.

Rod   A table for two.

Waiter   What . . . now?

Rod   Yes. We're hungry.

Waiter   Are you sure?

Pippa   We can always come back later . . .

Rod   I'm starving. I could eat a horse.

Waiter	Really? With chips and gravy?
Pippa	Pardon?
Waiter	Just a joke.
Rod	Where shall we sit?
Waiter	In the corner.
Pippa	It's very dark.
Waiter	I'll light a candle.

[*They go to a dark table in the corner and sit down*]

Pippa	It's a bit cold, too.
Waiter	I'll light two candles.
Rod	Can you put the light on?
Waiter	No. No, I can't. Not at all.
Pippa	Why not?
Waiter	There's a power cut.
Rod	A power cut?
Pippa	How can you cook with no power?
Waiter	Gas. Or salad. We do a very nice salad.
Rod	It's too cold for that.
Waiter	You can have it with an extra candle.
Pippa	We want hot food.
Waiter	Soup. We do a very nice pea soup.
Rod	Soup is a bit dull.

Pippa	True – we could have soup at home.
Waiter	Not OUR soup. It's won prizes.
Rod	Really? Where?
Waiter	Crufts.
Pippa	Crufts? That's a dog show.
Waiter	Is it? Er . . . it's poodle soup.
Rod	Poodle soup?
Pippa	Not poodle!
Waiter	Pot noodle. Not poodle – pot noodle.
Rod	Pot noodle?
Waiter	Pot noodle soup. Yes, that's it. I'll get the menu. [*He leaves*]
Pippa	I'm not sure about this place.
Rod	Don't worry. They say the chef is good.
Pippa	No one else is in here. That's a bad sign.
Rod	It will soon fill up. We're early.
Pippa	I think we should go.
Rod	Not now. I need to tell you something . . .

[*The waiter returns with the menu*]

Waiter	Here we are. Shall I take your brolly, miss?
Pippa	No thanks.
Waiter	But we need something to stir the soup. Just a joke!

6

Rod	Can we have a drink while we look at the menu?
Waiter	Yes, if I can find a clean glass.
Pippa	I'll have a tomato juice. With.
Waiter	With?
Rod	Yes, she wants it with.
Waiter	With what?
Pippa	I always have it with.
Waiter	Oh, I see, yes . . . with a glass. It's very messy if you don't have tomato juice with a glass.
Rod	She wants it with sauce and ice. I'll have the same.
Waiter	Fine. I won't be a jiff. [*He leaves*]
Pippa	Let's go now. Come on.
Rod	No. Listen. I've got to tell you . . .
Pippa	Tell me what?
Rod	It's time you knew something . . .
Pippa	What?
Rod	I've been meaning to tell you for a while . . .
Pippa	Well, hurry up then.
Rod	I don't want anyone else to hear.
Pippa	There's no one about for miles!
Rod	You can never be sure.

Pippa	Who's going to creep up on us here?

[*The waiter returns*]

Waiter	Here we are.
Pippa	Aah! You scared me!
Waiter	One tomato juice.
Pippa	We asked for two.
Waiter	Did you? I don't think so.
Rod	Yes we did. I asked to have the same.
Waiter	That's right. Here it is. The same one for both of you. Are you ready for a starter?
Pippa	Come on, Rod. Let's not stay . . . [*She is getting ready to leave*]
Rod	Fish. I'll have the fish.
Pippa	But Rod . . .
Rod	Pippa, it's urgent. I've got to tell you.
Waiter	The fish starters are very good.
Pippa	Oh, very well. Fish it is then.
Waiter	So it's a cod for Rod and a kipper for Pippa! A nice plaice we've got here! Joke. [*He leaves*]
Pippa	A nice place? It gives me the creeps.
Rod	Never mind. You've got to listen to me . . .
Pippa	Yes – what is it you need to say?
Rod	I can't keep it to myself any longer . . .

Pippa	Then tell me. I'm listening.
Rod	It's a secret.
Pippa	There's no one around. Go ahead.
Rod	The thing is . . .
Pippa	Aah!
Rod	What's the matter?
Pippa	Down there! On the carpet!
Rod	Where?
Pippa	There's a dark patch. It looks like . . . blood.
Rod	It must be red wine. Don't worry.
Pippa	And look at the candle. It's gross.
Rod	It looks like . . . bite marks.
Pippa	There's a tooth stuck in the wax.
Rod	And a meat axe is stuck in the next table.
Pippa	With a finger in the ashtray. Look!

[*The waiter returns*]

Waiter	It's a fish finger, miss.
Pippa	Aah! You scared me! Fish don't have fingers.
Waiter	Not if they come in here! That's a joke. It's squid.
Rod	What's it doing in the ashtray?
Waiter	It's a tip. I often get five or six squid in tips.

Rod	What?
Pippa	It's gross.
Waiter	Just a joke. We had a theme night here last night. It was a horror night.
Pippa	Well, we don't like it.
Waiter	Very sorry. We haven't had time to clear up.
Rod	Can't you get a bit of light in here?
Waiter	Oh no. We can't do that.
Pippa	Well, can't you make it a bit warmer?
Waiter	Sorry, it's the power cut. And I'm afraid to tell you that the fish is off.
Rod	Off?
Waiter	Yes, off. It's gone.
Pippa	Gone?
Waiter	It was the cat. It ate the lot.
Rod	In that case, I'll have steak.
Pippa	They can't cook it well if there's no power.
Rod	Then I'll have it rare.
Pippa	Are you sure?
Rod	Yes, I like rare steak.
Waiter	I'm afraid the steak is very rare here. There isn't any. It's so rare, it's off.
Pippa	Don't say the cat got that as well.

Waiter	Oh no. Certainly not. Never.
Rod	That's a relief.
Waiter	It was the dog.
Rod	The fish is off. The steak is off. The power is off. What else is off?
Waiter	The dog.
Pippa	The dog is off?
Waiter	Yes. The steak was bad.
Rod	Then I insist on seeing the chef.
Waiter	Sorry. He's off too.
Pippa	What do you mean?
Waiter	He ate something that upset him.
Rod	What was it? Nothing on the menu, I hope.
Waiter	Oh no. It wasn't food.
Pippa	If it wasn't food, what was it?
Waiter	Wire.
Rod	Wire?
Waiter	Flex. He bit the flex at the back of the cooker. That's why the power went off.
Pippa	What was he doing behind the cooker?
Waiter	Trying to catch a rat. But it got away and hid.
Pippa	[*To Rod*] I think it's time we went.

Rod	You're right. I wish we'd never come in. [*They move towards the door*]
Waiter	Oh no, you can't go! Not yet.
Rod	Why not? This place is awful.
Waiter	But I'm dying to know.
Pippa	Dying to know what?
Waiter	Rod's secret. I've got to know what it is.
Pippa	Come on, Rod. I can't stand this place.
Rod	I'll gladly tell you my secret. It's simple.
Pippa	No, tell me later.
Rod	I was going to tell you I'd left my wallet at home and we'd have to run out without paying.
Waiter	But what about your tomato juice?
Pippa	We're not paying for it. It didn't taste very nice anyway.
Waiter	I'm not surprised. I'll tell you my secret now. It wasn't tomato juice.
Pippa	WHAT?
Waiter	Just a little something I made before the power went off.
Rod	What do you mean?
Waiter	Well, how was I to know the rat hid in the blender?

[*They freeze – their faces say it all!*]

Tricky Main Course

Scene: Rod and Pippa enter a gloomy pub.

Rod	This pub will do.
Pippa	It doesn't look very nice.
Rod	It doesn't matter. It's out of the rain.
Pippa	I don't think it's open.
Rod	It's somewhere to sit. I need to talk to you.
Pippa	I don't like the smell.
Rod	It's fine. I just need to talk.
Pippa	There's a better pub over the road.
Rod	I need to tell you something.

[*A waiter appears as if from nowhere. Pippa jumps*]

Waiter	Can I help you?
Pippa	Aah! You scared me.
Rod	A table for two.
Waiter	What . . . now?
Rod	Yes. We're hungry.
Waiter	Are you sure?

Pippa	We can always come back later . . .
Rod	I'm starving. I could eat a horse.
Waiter	Really? With chips and gravy?
Pippa	Pardon?
Waiter	Just a joke.
Rod	Where shall we sit?
Waiter	In the corner.
Pippa	It's very dark.
Waiter	I'll light a candle.

[*They go to a dark table in the corner and sit down*]

Pippa	It's a bit cold, too.
Waiter	I'll light two candles.
Rod	Can you put the light on?
Waiter	No. No, I can't. Not at all.
Pippa	Why not?
Waiter	There's a power cut.
Rod	A power cut?
Pippa	How can you cook with no power?
Waiter	Gas. Or salad. We do a very nice salad.
Rod	It's too cold for that.
Waiter	You can have it with an extra candle.
Pippa	We want hot food.

14

Waiter	Curry. We do a very nice hot curry.
Rod	How hot?
Waiter	Put it this way – if you eat it, don't sneeze.
Pippa	Why not?
Waiter	You could weld your teeth, melt all your fillings and scorch the curtains.
Rod	Maybe no to the curry. Can we see the menu?
Waiter	The menu? Are you sure?
Pippa	What about the chef's special?
Waiter	The chef's special?
Pippa	Yes, the chef's special.
Waiter	You may think so but he seems pretty normal to me.
Pippa	No, I mean is there something special on the menu?
Waiter	Not really. There's just a pea stuck to this one. [*He hands them a menu*]
Pippa	What about puddings?
Waiter	The chef's best is Death by Chocolate.
Pippa	That sounds good.
Rod	Can we have a drink while we're waiting?
Waiter	A drink? You want a drink?
Pippa	Yes. That would be nice.

Waiter	It may take a while.
Rod	Can I have a wine?
Waiter	You can moan as much as you like but it will still take a while.
Pippa	Make that two.
Waiter	Two what?
Pippa	Two wines. White.
Waiter	White?
Rod	Dry.
Waiter	Dry?
Pippa	Is that a problem?
Waiter	A problem? Er . . . well . . . er . . . I'll be as quick as I can. [*He leaves*]
Pippa	What an odd person.
Rod	Strange.
Pippa	There's not a soul about.
Rod	Right. Now I can tell you.
Pippa	Tell me what?
Rod	I've been waiting all day.
Pippa	What for?
Rod	For this moment.
Pippa	Really?

16

Rod	I need to tell you.
Pippa	Well, go on then.
Rod	Right. Get ready. The thing is . . .
Pippa	Get it off your chest.
Rod	I'll come straight to the point . . .

[*The waiter returns with two empty glasses*]

Waiter	I'll come straight to the point . . . I'm new here. Here you are.
Pippa	The glasses are empty.
Waiter	You wanted them dry. This is my first night.
Rod	Can we order food?
Waiter	I'll do what I can. I've never done this before.
Pippa	Do you serve trout?
Waiter	I'll serve anyone, miss.
Rod	What about a vegetable?
Waiter	Yes, I'll serve you as well.
Rod	I'd like chips.
Waiter	Chips are off. No power.
Pippa	I'd love a pizza.
Waiter	Tricky. Have you got a mobile?
Pippa	Yes. In my handbag.
Waiter	In that case you can phone for one.

Rod	Look, this is stupid. What can you cook?
Waiter	Egg. We can do you an egg. Or toast.
Pippa	I could have that at home.
Waiter	Not the way we do it.
Rod	What about the stir-fry?
Waiter	With prawns?
Rod	Yes.
Waiter	And cashew nuts?
Pippa	Yes.
Waiter	And bamboo shoots, soy sauce and fried rice?
Rod	Great. That sounds great.
Waiter	It's off.
Pippa	Come on Rod, let's go. [*She is getting ready to leave*]
Waiter	I'm only joking. I'll see what I can do. [*He leaves*]
Pippa	I still think we should go. This place is mad.
Rod	But let me tell you first.
Pippa	What do you need to tell me?
Rod	Will you promise me?
Pippa	Promise you what?
Rod	Promise you won't be mad.

18

Pippa	Sshh. What was that noise? Like a hiss.
Rod	It must be the gas.
Pippa	No, it was like a panting noise.
Rod	Maybe the gas is tired. Never mind. Listen . . .
Pippa	Aah! I just saw something.
Rod	Where? What? When?
Pippa	I'm sure I saw a knife in the kitchen.
Rod	Pippa, it's a kitchen!
Pippa	It was sticking out of a body.
Rod	A body? Don't talk daft. You can't see a thing in here. It's so dark.
Pippa	It had a chef's hat on. The waiter was dragging it across the kitchen. [*She stands up*]
Rod	Where are you going?
Pippa	I'm going to the loo. [*She leaves*]
Rod	[*To himself*] She's just making a fuss. It's not that bad here when you get used to it . . .

[*The waiter returns*]

Waiter	A bit of bad news.
Rod	Don't tell me the stir-fry is off.
Rod	Yes. So is the chef.
Rod	What do you mean?

Waiter	It's the chef's night off.
Rod	So what are you going to do?
Waiter	Here's a ham salad. [*He puts a plate on the table*]
Rod	That's just a bit of old meat on a leaf.
Waiter	It's the best I can do. It's chef's night off.
Rod	It's not even ham.
Waiter	Tongue. That's what it said on the tin.
Rod	Pippa won't eat tongue. It's been inside a cow's mouth! What a thought!
Waiter	I'll get her an egg instead.
Rod	What's that noise?
Waiter	Him. The chef's in the freezer.
Rod	Shall I help you get him out?
Waiter	No thanks.
Rod	Why not?
Waiter	Because I just put him in.
Rod	But you'll kill him!
Waiter	That's the idea. I hit him over the head with a slab of chocolate.
Rod	That's murder!
Waiter	That's right. Death by Chocolate!

[*Pippa returns*]

20

Pippa	We must go now, Rod.
Waiter	Oh no you don't! Stay right there. Both of you. Sit there and don't move!
Pippa	I told you this wasn't a nice place.
Waiter	See this knife? I'll use it.
Pippa	I knew it was a mistake coming here.
Waiter	Very true. I was in the middle of robbing this place. I don't work here at all. I was just about to get away with the cash. You fools!
Rod	So what happens now?
Waiter	I'll have to kill you before I get away. I turned out the lights but you've seen too much.
Pippa	Why didn't you lock the door?
Waiter	Nobody's perfect.
Pippa	I am. I've just phoned the police on my mobile. They're on their way.
Waiter	Then I'll have to kill you first.
Pippa	Not before I pop my paper bag . . . [*She takes a paper bag from her handbag and pops it in the waiter's face*]
Waiter	Aah! [*Falling to the floor and screaming*]
Pippa	Lucky I took the pepper pot with me and made a little bomb! Quick Rod, put the table cloth over his head.

Rod   I can hear the police car. Pippa, you're a star!

[*They tie a cloth around the choking waiter*]

Pippa   By the way, what were you trying to tell me?

Rod   Er . . . tricky. I've changed my mind now.

Pippa   Tell me.

Rod   I was trying to say it was all over. I was going to move away. But not now.

Pippa   Why not?

Rod   You. Me. This. The police. You're great!

Pippa   So what will you say to the police?

Rod   Simple. 'Pippa picked the pepper pot to pop it in her pocket and packed it in a paper packet!'

Pippa   That's tricky to say.

Rod   This isn't. Let's go for a proper meal.

Pippa   Great. I'm starving.

Rod   How about this bit of meat curling at the edges.

Pippa   A tongue-twister to end all tongue-twisters . . .

Rod   Yeah. Like this. Pippa's a proper poppet! Her paper pepper-popper popped pepper on the porky purple pop-eyed pimply pickpocket! PHEW!

Sticky Pudding

Scene: Rod and Pippa enter a gloomy pub.

Rod This pub will do.

Pippa It doesn't look very nice.

Rod It doesn't matter. It's out of the rain.

Pippa I don't think it's open.

Rod It's somewhere to sit. I need to talk to you.

Pippa I don't like the smell.

Rod It's fine. I just need to talk.

Pippa There's a better pub over the road.

Rod I need to tell you something.

[The waiter appears as if from nowhere. Pippa jumps]

Waiter Can I help you?

Pippa Aah! You scared me.

Rod A table for two.

Waiter What . . . now?

Rod Yes. We're hungry.

Waiter Are you sure?

Pippa We can always come back later . . .

Rod I'm starving. I could eat a horse.

Waiter	Really? With chips and gravy?
Pippa	Pardon?
Waiter	Just a joke.
Rod	Where shall we sit?
Waiter	In the corner.
Pippa	It's very dark.
Waiter	I'll light a candle.

[*They go to a dark table in the corner and sit down*]

Pippa	It's a bit cold, too.
Waiter	I'll light two candles.
Rod	Can you put the light on?
Waiter	No. No, I can't. Not at all.
Pippa	Why not?
Waiter	There's a power cut.
Rod	A power cut?
Pippa	How can you cook with no power?
Waiter	Gas. Or salad. We do a very nice salad.
Rod	It's too cold for that.
Waiter	You can have it with an extra candle.
Pippa	We want hot food.
Waiter	Hot pot. We do a very nice hot pot.
Pippa	What's in it?

Waiter	Goat and carrots. It's a sort of stew.
Rod	I don't think so. I prefer food from the East.
Waiter	Then our Eastern Hot Pot is just the job. It's a spicy stew. You can taste the East.
Pippa	What's in it?
Waiter	Camel and carrots.
Rod	No thanks. I like Chinese food.
Waiter	No problem. How about Fu Stew?
Rod	Fu Stew? What's in it?
Waiter	Rice and carrots.
Pippa	You seem to like carrots here.
Waiter	We need them to help us see in the dark. The fuse keeps blowing.
Rod	You've got a fault somewhere.
Waiter	True. It's the chef. It's his fault! He spills drink all over the place. It gets in the fuse box and blows. It costs us a fortune in candles.
Pippa	Has your chef got a drink problem?
Waiter	He's always drunk. We keep losing him. He's hard to find in the dark. He's just gone off!
Rod	It can't be a safe kitchen.
Pippa	True. I think I'll skip the main course.
Rod	How about a pudding?

Pippa	Does the chef make good puddings?
Waiter	Oh yes. He spills a lot of drink in those, too. I'll get a menu. [*He leaves*]
Pippa	This is a bit of a funny old place.
Rod	Never mind. It's somewhere to talk. Listen . . .
Pippa	Yes, what is it?
Rod	Well, Pippa . . . I want to give you a ring.
Pippa	A ring? For me? Oh Rod, how lovely.
Rod	Pardon? Why are you going all soppy?
Pippa	A ring! I had no idea! Why don't you get on your knees and do it properly?
Rod	Sorry?
Pippa	I'm so happy! I hope you didn't spend too much on it. How many carats?
Rod	I'm not having carrots.
Pippa	Let's order some champagne.
Rod	Are you sure?
Pippa	Of course. It's not every day we get engaged.
Rod	Eh?
Pippa	I can't wait to tell all my friends.
Rod	Tell them what?
Pippa	How you brought me here tonight to propose!
Rod	Er . . .

Pippa	I can't wait to see the ring. Where is it?
Rod	Er . . .
Pippa	Tell you what . . . give it to me in a sec. I'm nipping to the loo to have a good cry. When I come back, you can get on one knee and give me the ring. I won't be long. [*She leaves*]
Rod	Oh heck!

[*The waiter returns*]

Waiter	Here we are.
Rod	What am I going to do? I don't believe it!
Waiter	Yes, it's a hard choice, isn't it?
Rod	I can't face it!
Waiter	You can always have a scoop of ice cream.
Rod	No. Her. Pippa. She thinks I want to marry her. She thinks I've got a ring. A ring!
Waiter	The sticky toffee pudding is very nice.
Rod	It's not as sticky as the mess I'm in! What can I do?
Waiter	You can always try a bit of both.
Rod	A bit of both?
Waiter	Yes. Jam roly-poly and custard – with a spot of ice cream. What do you think?
Rod	What do I think? What do I think? I think I'm in it up to my neck!

Waiter	Our puddings aren't quite that big, sir.
Rod	Me and my mouth!
Waiter	Yes, it will come in very handy for the trifle.
Rod	I only wanted to ask if I could give her a phone call later. To tell her if I've got a new job. I said, 'Can I give you a ring?' She thinks I mean a WEDDING RING!
Waiter	Oops.
Rod	If I tell her it's a mistake, she'll go mad. You should see her when she's mad! She's scary.
Waiter	Leave it with me. [*He leaves*]
Rod	[*To himself*] What am I going to say? Oh no, here she is.

[*Pippa returns*]

Pippa	[*She sits down and dabs her eyes*] I'm so happy, Rod. I'll be a good wife to you. Always.
Rod	Yes, but . . .
Pippa	We'll have a party. I want the world to know.
Rod	. . . the thing is . . .
Pippa	Are you going to give me the ring now?
Rod	. . . you see . . . I need to phone you later to tell you if my letter came today.
Pippa	What letter?

Rod	For a new job. I might have to move away.
Pippa	That's OK. We can get a flat. Together.
Rod	Er . . . um . . . well . . .

[*The waiter returns with a silver tray*]

Waiter	Here we are. A bottle of our best champagne, ice, a red rose and, on this cushion – a ring!
Rod	What?
Pippa	Let me see! It's lovely. Oh Rod, it's so perfect. [*She gives him a big kiss*]
Waiter	Anything else, sir?
Rod	Er . . . er . . . um . . . well . . .
Pippa	Yes. I'll have the sticky toffee pudding. Or maybe the sherry trifle. It's hard to say.
Waiter	So is this: the sherry is off. The chef's gone off with the sherry. He might be in the shed where we keep the shellfish fresh.
Pippa	That sounds a bit tricky to say, too!
Waiter	And this. The chef's sure to have shut the sherry in the fresh shellfish shed.
Pippa	The chef's sure to have shut the sherry in the fresh shellfish shed?
Waiter	Yes, the chef's sure to have shut the sherry in the fresh shellfish shed.
Rod	Can you get our food? Pippa and I must talk.

Waiter	Very well. [*He leaves, giving Rod a very big wink*]
Pippa	Rod, I'm so glad you brought me here.
Rod	Well, the thing is you see . . .
Pippa	The candles, the napkins, the long dark table cloths down to the floor . . .
Rod	. . . but . . . well, it . . . what I mean is . . .
Pippa	I never knew you could be so romantic.
Rod	. . . well no, I know . . . er . . . you see . . .
Pippa	Not only have you given me this lovely ring . . .
Rod	. . . well, that's the thing. I need to tell you . . .
Pippa	. . . since we first sat down, I knew you loved me.
Rod	Really? What gave you that idea?
Pippa	Your touch.
Rod	Eh?
Pippa	The way you've held my hand under the table.
Rod	But I haven't . . .
Pippa	The way you've rubbed your foot on mine.
Rod	Have I?
Pippa	And the way you keep brushing my leg.
Rod	I had no idea . . .
Pippa	And now you're all mine! For ever. I think I'm going to cry again. Excuse me! [*She runs out*]
Rod	Waiter! Waiter!

30

Waiter	The pudding is on its way, sir.
Rod	Never mind the pudding. What's going on?
Waiter	Going on? Didn't you like the ring I gave you?
Rod	Where did it come from?
Waiter	You'd be surprised what we keep in our 'lost pot'. People leave all sorts of things here. Buttons, false teeth, watches, rings, nose-studs . . .
Rod	But what do I owe you?
Waiter	It will all be on the bill, sir.
Rod	It's all come as a bit of a shock.
Waiter	You were good to me about our chef's night off. So I wanted to be kind to you.
Rod	I only met Pippa last week.
Waiter	She must like you.
Rod	She said I was being very friendly . . . under the table.
Waiter	Under the table?
Rod	Yes. She said I was touching her leg . . .
Waiter	Then we'd better take a look. [*He lifts the table cloth*] So that's where the chef's gone. He's asleep with a bottle of port under your table. We'd better let him sleep it off.
Rod	I wish I could sleep it off. I only came in for a hot pot. I'll be leaving with a wife!

Waiter	You could always tell her it was a mistake.
Rod	I could never do that. No, I'll make a run for it . . . [*He starts to run but falls to the floor*]
Waiter	Are you all right, sir?
Rod	My shoe laces are tied together!
Waiter	Chef's little joke. He always does that. It stops people leaving without paying. Here's the bill.

[*Pippa returns*]

Pippa	What are you doing down there, Rod? Get up! You're coming with me. I've phoned for a taxi on my mobile. I'm taking you to meet Mother.
Rod	Yes, dear.
Pippa	Then we'll buy my wedding dress. Now, get out your wallet and pay the waiter. Make sure you give him a very big tip. What's the name of this pub, anyway?

[*Rod stares at the huge bill. He pays in a daze*]

Waiter	It was The Pony and Trap. But tonight the pony is off.
Pippa	The pony is off? Everything is off here!
Waiter	They took down some letters on the sign to paint them. Tonight we're just The Trap.
Pippa	What a daft name. It doesn't make sense.
Waiter	I think it does for Rod! Good night!